AMATEUR'S GUI...

WALTER LORCH

Drawings by Eddy Lawrence

J. A. ALLEN
LONDON & NEW YORK

Lorch, Walter F
    Amateur's guide to foaling.
    1. Horse breeding
    I. Title
    636.1'08'2   SF291

    ISBN 0-85131-302-7

Published in Great Britain in 1979 by
J. A. Allen & Company Limited,
1, Lower Grosvenor Place, Buckingham Palace Road,
London, SWIW 0EL,
and in the United States of America by
Sporting Book Center, Inc.,
Canaan,
New York, NY12029.
Printed in Great Britain.

FOREWORD

Walter Lorch was first to introduce closed-circuit television for mare observation. This helped him to gain insight into the behaviour of a mare prior to foaling and gain knowledge of the symptoms indicating imminent birth. In 1960 the author imported into this country the first Trakehner stallion from Germany and two mares of famous Trakehner blood lines. From this small beginning evolved the Anglo-Trakehner, now a fixed breed in the fifth generation.

A great deal has been written on foaling but here the author has come up with a simple format of direct and positive assistance to the amateur breeder. The information is brief and to the point and the presentation in diary form is easy to follow. There is no jargon and advice is given with the logical clarity of the true professional. The result is a practical guide leading the amateur from stallion selection through birth to weaning.

Maj.-Gen. Sir Evelyn Fanshawe, C.B., C.B.E., D.L.
(Past President of the Hunters' Improvement Society)

ACKNOWLEDGEMENTS

I wish to thank the publisher of *Heavy Horse and Driving* for permission to reproduce in book form the article which first appeared in that magazine. For his superb illustrations I thank Eddy Lawrence. The photograph on the front cover is reproduced by courtesy of The Muschamp Stud.

CONTENTS

INTRODUCTION

To whom it may concern . . . . . . a ghastly, platitudinos phrase, but unavoidable here. You are not concerned and please don't read on if you put mares into foal year by year or if you run a stud farm. Really that crystallizes in a somewhat negative form the readers who will enjoy and, hopefully, benefit from this book.

Having kept out the professionals, the regulars and the know-alls, I must now define my readers. You, who love horses (of course), who has a mare, a friend for years and would like her foal to continue the friendship bond. She is not too young at three or too old at twelve. You, who has a filly and cannot really do much with her until she is at least four and you might as well make her pregnant and share with her the delights of motherhood. I have been present at hundreds of births at least and am I bored, blasé or indifferent? No, positively not. It's a miracle every time, an experience, private, personal and for ever elating. Beware though of the Cassandras, just "good friends" or those who lost the foal. We all know the type. They thrive on sick gossip and revel in the amputation of Mr. Jones's leg. Don't listen. Read.

DECEMBER

Conveniently this is the time for giving. Scan horse bookshops for material on breeding and foaling and finally decide on the book which will form the basis of your own management from conception, through birth, to weaning.

My own recommendation is two books which are both published by J. A. Allen & Company Limited, 1, Lower Grosvenor Place, Buckingham Palace Road, London, SWIW 0EL:

Mares, Foals and Foaling, by Andrist; and *Horse Breeding and Stud Management,* by Wynmalen.

In conjunction with this book they will give you the "know-how" you require based on their authors' wide experience, in good English and without padding.

JANUARY, FEBRUARY, MARCH

Stallion selection and preparation of mare

You have made up your mind — your filly is going to be covered and now is the time to select the stallion. Now, not later. This is going to be a time-consuming job, with much travel. Already you have in your mind a picture of the foal, the future member of your family. It's looks, temperament and action have been discussed at length. You know of course the good and bad points of the mother, but all your projections remain theory unless you go and see the potential father and, most important, his progeny.

Any good stud owner will be delighted to show you his stallion. Watch the horse's reaction to man, his manners, conformation and action. Observe and take in the layout, cleanliness and atmosphere of the place. This should form a vital link in your final decision. Run a mile if you see barbed wire. Go and visit the horse's young stock. Quite likely some of his yearlings will be on the farm. Then make a special point of contacting one of his three-year-olds. Where these facilities are not given freely and with enthusiasm delete this stud from your list, however much you may like the horse. A stallion owner who is un-cooperative at this stage will act with similar indifference at cover time.

When you have made your choice ask for a nomination form and complete the questionnaire conscientiously. This will help the stud groom a great deal when the time comes. Fix the mare's arrival for April and have her examined (swabbed) by your vet during her first heat in March. This time sequence is essential for maiden and barren mares, as it will put you back at least a month if the vet has to clear an infection. But, you will say, I want a May or June foal when the grass and weather are at their best. Why send her so early? Well, life and nature cannot be programmed just like that. Your mare is unlikely to come into oestrus on schedule once she has left home and is even more unlikely to conceive right-away. I have seen too many disappointed mare owners who insisted on sending their maidens late expecting the first leap to bring the desired result. I feel strongly on this point and will not accept mares after May without foal at foot. The covering season ends on the 31st July.

One final point: make sure your mare is fit, not fat, as her chance of conception decreases in proportion to unnecessary weight.

APRIL TO JULY

Sending your mare to stud, pregnancy tests, bringing her home

Your mare has now been swabbed and certified "clean". Don't wait until she shows signs of being in season again before you take her to the stallion. Not later than two weeks after swabbing, which was carried out during oestrus, make arrangements with the stud owner to receive her. Worm the mare before she leaves. In this way she will have time to settle in her new environment, make friends and discuss her problems with the other mares and get used to the staff. You will be asked how long you would like her to stay. I suggest you leave her for a minimum of twenty-five days after the last service, because she is likely to be in foal if she has not "returned" (come into oestrus again) by then.

If you live a fair distance away let her remain for a further twenty-one days for safety. If she holds through this second season, there is every reason to believe she is pregnant. At this point, at least forty-two days after service, the stud's vet should carry out a manual pregnancy test. If it proves positive you may take her home.

JULY ONWARDS

Food, exercise and observance

If the mare has been ridden regularly do not hesitate to continue, but no jumping, sudden starts and stops please. Watch her weight and do not let her get fat. There is a tendency for overweight mares to abort or absorb their foal. During the first half of pregnancy the foetus grows only slowly. If your grazing is good no extra food should be needed until the autumn, except for thoroughbreds. In October begin to add hay gradually and a proprietry brand of stud cubes, with a vitamin compound. This book is a guide and not a manual and to recommend specific weights is outside its scope. Observation and common sense are the only reliable guides. The maxim of "what looks right is right" applies to your mare. Food intake should equal and not exceed the body's demands. Exercise, good, not rich, pasture and later best quality hard hay and clean oats or stud cubes should be fed in small amounts and increased as the foetus grows.

SIX WEEKS BEFORE FOALING

Preparation of the stable or paddock, feeding, observance, equipment and the foaling bucket

We must now define the foaling date for the purpose of this book. Statistics, opinion and advice vary enormously, but I have found 340 days from conception an acceptable average. There are completely normal births two weeks before, and up to three weeks after this highly arbitrary 340 days period. Most maidens and irregular breeders are late, few foal early, fewer still foal on time. Your motto: "Be prepared".

For a 15.2 hh mare the minimum stable size to serve as a foaling box should be ten by twelve feet and considerably larger for a heavier and taller mare. The life of your foal and the health of the dam are directly dependent on the cleanliness of the foaling box. Six weeks before the due date clear the box

Meticulous hose down and disinfection of foaling box are vital.

out completely, hose down ceiling, walls and floor, spraying carefully into cracks and corners. Scrub all surfaces with disinfectant. Allow to dry for twenty-four hours and apply disinfectant once more with a pressure sprayer. Close the box for a week and repeat the scrubbing and pressure spraying.

Four weeks before foaling, bed down with super clean straw and muck out with particular care and keep dogs — in fact everybody — away from this labour ward. At the danger of being called a fusspot I say once more: carry out this procedure with infinite care. Navel or joint-ill is the most common cause of death in the young foal. Organisms enter the open navel (umbilicus) mostly because of inattention to basic hygiene.

Prepare the foaling paddock.

Foaling Out

If you have no suitable stable there is nothing wrong with foaling out. In fact most mares prefer it. A well fenced paddock without barbed wire is the only requirement. But beware of the ditch, running just outside the fence. Somehow mares like to foal in awkward spots and I heard of the sad case where the newly-born foal rolled straight through the fence into a stream and was drowned. Once more inspect your paddock with the impossible in mind and all will be well.

FIVE WEEKS BEFORE FOALING

Feeding

Five weeks prior to foaling change to a softer diet. Do this gradually by reducing the oats or stud cubes so that at foaling time the hard food intake is only two-fifths of what it was five weeks before. Also beginning five weeks prior to the great day give a bran mash as the last daily meal. Once a week mix a heaped tablespoon of Epsom Salt into the feed. Careful observation of the droppings will be your guide: they should be loose and resemble those of a grass-fed horse. Make a point of achieving this as correct feeding immediately prior to birth plays a vital part during the foal's first few days. Too many amateurs increase the weight of corn right up to foaling. As a result the newly-born foal will have difficulty in passing droppings, a symptom which I will come back to later on.

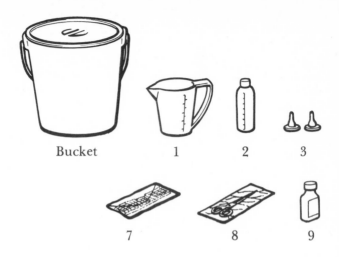

Bucket   1   2   3

7   8   9

Foaling Equipment

Having prepared stable and paddock we now assemble the equipment for foaling. Buy a 2 gallon plastic bucket with a well-fitting lid. Don't use an old one, as even careful cleaning will not destroy the established organisms in the cracks of the plastic. Now buy the following:

1. One 500 ml polythene jug.
2. One baby's feeding bottle.
3. Two calf-teats. (Pierce one. Test it for flow. Liquid should run easily when bottle is squeezed.) Put in polythene bag and seal it.
4. One small jar of Vaseline.
5. One enema syringe.
6. One 240 ml bottle of liquid paraffin BP.
7. A 12in. linen strip about ¼in. wide, boiled for sterilisation. Put this in an envelope and seal it.

14

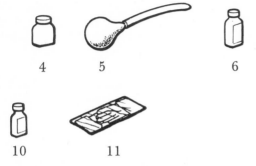

4   5   6

10   11

8. Scissors. Sterilise them, put in an envelope and seal it.
9. One 7 g dispenser of antiseptic dusting powder (B-F-I Bismuth-Formic-Iodide Compound).
10. One 25 ml bottle of Iodine tincture BP. (If your chemist does not stock items 9 and 10 ask him to order these. Most Boots shops have them).
11. Surgical gloves. (If you cannot get these from your chemist, ask your vet).

Place these things in the bucket, starting with item 1, so that they will be easy to hand in the order in which they are needed. Let me say at once that you are likely to use items 9, 10 and 11 only for a normal foaling. This is why they are placed uppermost. Close the lid and put bucket in a new polythene bag — a bin liner is ideal for this.

Now collect the following:

> One 2 gallon bucket (this need not be new)
> One tablet of soap
> One small bottle of Dettol
> One hand towel
> One bath towel
> One torch
> Some bailing twine
> One overall
> A large card with the telephone number of your vet — and a bottle to celebrate the birth.

This completes the foaling equipment.

TWO WEEKS TO GO

Observe and don't Fuss

You are well prepared: stable, paddock and foaling aids are ready for the great event. Thousands of words have been written and uttered by the eminent, the experts and those who think they are, helping you how to predict the day and time. Those scribes who are honest all agree at least on one point: there is no way of forecasting the birthday. This author will

Waxed up.

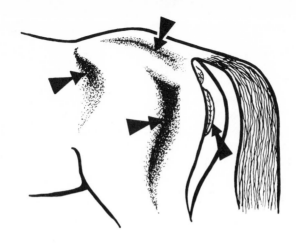

Foaling imminent; dilated vaginal entry — collapsed muscles.

therefore list the signs as they appear and say quite
humbly that birth is imminent when one or more of
certain indicators are present: the udder grows and
feels hard and looks shiny, a sticky off-white cork
forms on the nipples (waxing), milk drips or runs.
These symptoms may start two weeks or even earlier
or just a day before birth and some mares do not
"leak" at all.

Other indications are a general softening and sinking of the muscles around the hind quarters. "Falling
in" or "poverty line" might be a good description.
But the most important and reliable sign is the softening and swelling of the vaginal lips. Normally the
texture, feel and appearance of the vaginal opening
is firm, tight and dry. Prior to birth it will be floppy,
soft and moist.

Enough said of the external signs. Throughout this book I have stressed the value of conscientious observance and by now your mare's behaviour pattern will be familiar to you. When birth is imminent this pattern is likely to change. Restlessness, pacing, seeing ghosts, scraping the straw to make a nest, sweating, showing dislike of stable confinement, getting down only to get up again, making lots of droppings, leaving you in no doubt that she is going to do great things quite soon. And others do nothing of the sort. When they are ready they just lie down and foal. Conclusions, advice, or just hints: yes, one only: be prepared.

FOALING

When to help, when to call the vet, the navel, the first suck, colostrum, bottle feeding, droppings, feeding the mother.

In the previous lines I have been vague in the extreme and, you may have thought, unhelpful. I make no apology. To act differently, to be categorical or even more definite would be sheer arrogance and misleading. The exact opposite applies to the subject of foaling. Once the actual birth cycle has started a clearly predictable sequence of happenings will take place. These I will describe now and in so doing will try to help you to act when your assistance is needed.

The Foaling Sequence

The mare lies down and places herself comfortably on her side. At intervals her head will bend towards her quarters and her nose touch her flanks. All this happens quietly. At this stage the vaginal lips are swollen and shiny. Quite quickly a blueish-white membrane rather like a balloon will protrude, burst and liquid will flow out (bursting of the water bag). The foaling cycle has commenced.

Wash and scrub your hands and arms. Wash and scrub again. Put on the overall. Place the foaling bucket and utensils nearby and a bale of straw near the stable door. Do not disturb the mare; move gently without haste.

The mare will get up quite a few times and then lie down again. Relax and observe. Next, the feet of the foal will appear, sometimes still covered by a membrane. Watch until they stick out some six inches. If the membrane is still intact break it by applying pressure to the foal's feet. It will tear easily.

The Normal Position

Move the tail upwards. You must now check whether the foal's position is normal, that is to say — head resting on the front feet. The time factor is important. If all is well no more than ten minutes will pass between the burst of the water bag and the appearance of feet and muzzle. Action: if all has progressed as described here, leave the stable, wash your hands again and continue to watch.

Malpresentation

If eleven minutes have gone since the water bag burst and your mare has strained hard to expel the foal but the front feet and muzzle have not come out, phone your vet at once. Don't dither, phone and tell him you suspect a malpresentation and need his

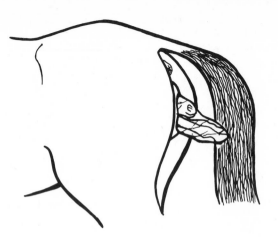

Position correct.

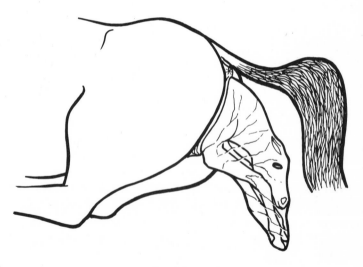

Shoulders out.

20

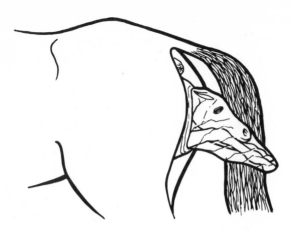

Head out; clear membranes from nostrils.

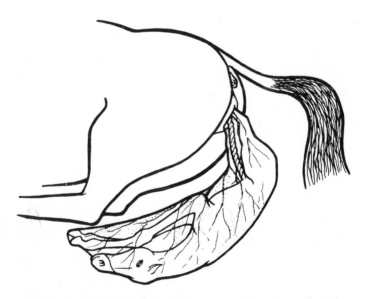

Gently pull foal towards mare's head. Don't break navel cord.

help now. Time is vital at this stage and delay is not permissable. Keep your mare soothed. Have soap, bucket and towel ready and act under the vet's instructions upon his arrival.

Apart from the man-modified thoroughbred racing machine, horses are efficient and easy foalers. Complications or twins are rare. This scribe continues to believe and base his advice on this assumption.

Labour and how you can help

The feet and muzzle are showing. Clear the foal's nostrils of mucus. The mare will now rest a while to gain strength for the next stages which consist of pushing the foal's head and large shoulders through the narrow vaginal passage.

Tying up the navel stump

When the navel cord breaks naturally bleeding from the stump is minimal. When for any reason whatsoever loss of blood through the umbilical opening continues, particularly when the foal moves, the stump should be tied. Don't rush to do this. Give it a few minutes and in most cases the bleeding will stop on its own. Don't be alarmed. A few squirts of blood may seem an awful lot, but are really only a few millilitres.

Should you decide to tie the stump act as follows. If possible ask someone to help. I have been reluctant to introduce an assistant as the standards of cleanliness demanded from you apply equally to your helper. He must wear clean overalls and be "scrubbed up". He does not, however, need surgical gloves. Ask him to hold down the foal. Put on the

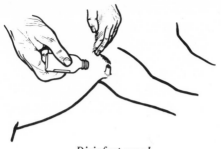

Disinfect navel.

Squeeze blood from navel stump.

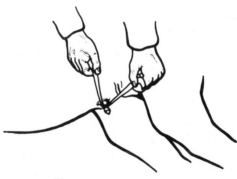

Tie up.

surgical gloves. Squeeze out the blood from the stump by holding it with the thumb and forefinger where it joins the body. Now move your fingers down the stump, applying firm pressure. In doing this you will clear the blood. Take the linen strip from its envelope and tie up as high as possible. Thereafter repeat the blood expelling action to get rid of any residue and apply iodine and powder as explained previously. Close the stable door, top and bottom and go away for forty minutes.

The first suck

If the foal is healthy and vigorous he will be hungry quite soon and search for milk all over the dam's body, exploring all but the right spot.

Eventually he will find the nipples and suck. In practice the time between birth and the first drink varies enormously. Some foals get up, search and find the supply within an hour, others get up, lie down and begin to drink only after six hours searching. And six hours is your limit. If the youngster has not sucked at birth plus six hours you must act — and act promptly and decisively.

Be very firm on this point, because there is no room for wishful thinking here. Sucking means that you have seen him drink. If you have not, act as follows: put a head collar on the mare, tie her up, or much better, ask your helper to hold her. Guide the foal gently, but decisively to the teats, encouraging his search for milk. Do this with infinite patience, permitting him to rest, allowing him to try "the other side" but drink he must. Unless he takes the colostrum, a translucent liquid, preceding the actual milk supply, the foal will be unable to combat infection, incapable of living a normal life and he will die sooner or later. He must — I repeat — take in the colostrum within seven hours from birth. The strong and eager foal will suck, if necessary with your help.

A weak or premature foal may make only feeble attempts at sucking, give up, lie down and fall asleep. His remaining strength and the will to live deteriorate amazingly fast.

Bottle Feeding

If the six hours have passed since birth and your efforts to make him drink have failed, act as follows: ask the assistant to hold the mare. Take from the foaling bucket the jug, feeding bottle, teat and Vaseline. Apply Vaseline to your hands to lessen friction and milk the dam into the polythene jug. Massage the udder downwards with firm pressure, changing into a squeeze — pull rhythm as your cupped hand approaches the nipple. Continue until you have collected 250 ml, empty it into the bottle and put on the teat. Tie up the mare and ask your assistant to leave.

If the foal is lying down, kneel down beside him, put a drop of milk from the bottle on to your forefinger and offer it. Let him suck for just three seconds, and follow up instantly with the teat, squeezing the bottle very gently to ease the flow. As the foal's sucking action increases, lessen the pressure on the bottle. Once he has sucked he will not look back. When he has emptied the bottle, leave, close the top and bottom door, wash and sterilize the jug, bottle and teat conscientiously. Return after twenty minutes (not later) and repeat the milking and feeding. Don't try to persuade the foal to drink from the mare at this stage. You will only upset and tire him.

At these first two feeds the colour of the mare's milk is translucent, particularly when it is first drawn. This is the colostrum, so vital to the foal's life. The third feed should again be given after twenty minutes and thereafter offer a further three feeds at intervals of forty minutes. Always wash and sterilize the untensils. By then the foal should be active, getting up frequently and show an interst in his surroundings. Most likely he will now search for the dam's milk supply and succeed. If not you may once more help him to achieve this. Squeeze some milk from the mare's teats on his nose and lips and he will take to natural feeding quite soon.

To sum up: success depends on the foal's vigour. If he remains listless after the second bottle call your vet. Delay is not permissable.

Droppings

Within a few hours of the foal's first suck he will make droppings. These first excreta are shiny black balls, held together to form a sausage. On straining, they should be released quite easily and will, if you correctly fed the dam prior to birth. If the foal strains again and again without success act as follows: take the enema syringe and bottle of liquid paraffin from the foaling bucket. Fill the enema, lubricate the plastic tube to lessen friction. Ask the assistant to hold the foal and gently guide the tube some two inches into the foal's anus. Allow the liquid to flow and withdraw the tube when the container is empty. Within an hour droppings will be passed.

THE MARE AFTER FOALING

The afterbirth. When to call the vet. Feeding

So far the foal has demanded most of your attention. Apart from the well deserved bran mash and tying up the afterbirth you have done nothing for the mare. Lift up her tail and push away the membranes hanging down from the vaginal entry. Look for tears at top and bottom which occur quite often. If the tear is ragged and more than a half-inch long, or longer, it should be stitched by the vet who may also give antibiotics against infection.

The afterbirth should come out soon after foaling. The mare will lie down and behave in a way not unsimilar to foaling. When the afterbirth has detached itself, take it from the stable and spread it out on the ground to check if it is complete. Don't worry if tiny bits are torn off but if sections are missing they are unlikely to come out on their own and retention will cause infection. Call the vet and keep the placenta for him to see. Also, if the placenta has not come away six hours from birth, veterinary aid is essential. Delay is not permissable.

Now make your own mare comfortable by sponging the encrusted areas of her hind quarters. Use only a thoroughly clean sponge and add Dettol to the warm water. Feeding routine after foaling is similar to that immediately before.

AND NOW THERE ARE TWO

If you missed the actual birth, which is not unusal if the mare foaled out, you should attend to foal and

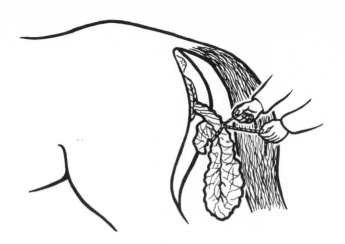

Tie up the placenta.

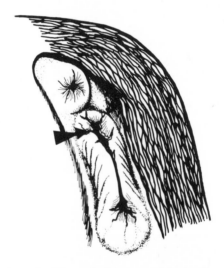

Look for tears in the vaginal entry. (Afterbirth omitted for clarity).

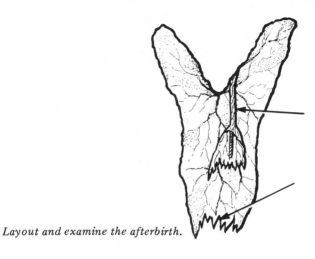

Layout and examine the afterbirth.

mare as soon as you arrive on the scene. Treatment of the foal's navel, supervision of his food intake and droppings and attention to the afterbirth can all be given in the paddock. If the placenta has come away search the field and examine it as described earlier. If you cannot find it, assume that a fox ate it — quite a common experience.

The First Outing

When the foal is two or three days old, and on a fine day, do not hesitate to let him out. After some days of confinement the mare is itching to have a run and grass will increase her milk production. It is always a good idea to lead the mare out on the lunge and give her the freedom of the paddock only when she has settled. Right from the start lead the foal. I find a stable rubber an ideal leading rein for the first few outings.

Start with an hour and increase the time daily until the tenth day when they can stay out all day. When the nights are no longer cold keep them out altogether.

Observance continues

Your vigilance should continue after birth. Prompt recognition of any unusual signs in either mare or foal will facilitate treatment. Inspect the foal's navel daily. The stump should be encrusted and dry on the third day. If it continues to discharge call the vet.

The foal should drink from both teats in turn and both udders should be soft to the touch. If one of them is hard and the teat is not wet and glossy there is trouble. Call the vet. If your mare feeds and looks well and produces plenty of milk do not worry if there is a slight discharge of blood and mucus from her vagina. It is quite normal for this to happen for some ten days.

Diarrhoea and Coughing

Watch the foal's droppings. During the mare's first season (foaling heat) some six to ten days after birth some foals have diarrhoea. This should stop when the dam "has gone off". Diarrhoea or scouring other than during the foaling heat is a killer. Foals' droppings should be soft but formed and light brown — never, never should they be yellow or liquid.

Make a habit of listening to the foal's breathing and if he coughs call the vet at once. I cannot possibly overstate the importance of close observation and instant action when unhealthy or unusual symptoms are noted. During the first few weeks the youngster's resistance is minimal and the change from vigorous health to listlessness may take place with dramatic speed. Remember that it has taken eleven months to produce this foal. He needs your help to grow into a healthy horse.

WEANING

A week before you intend to wean introduce the foal to oats or nuts. Some five months after birth is a good time to separate mother and foal. And if the dam is pregnant again do not delay this. If at all possible take the foal out of earshot. If there is an opportunity to put him in a paddock with another foal, or calves or a donkey do so.

Offer a few oats after separation and increase the ration as he eats up. Worm the foal. Company, regular feeding and a well fenced paddock are now his only requirements.

At weaning it is the dam who needs your help and careful watching. Where possible, move her to poor pasture. Do not curtail water supplies. Ten hours after separation feel her udders. If they are hard and tight or milk is running, relieve the pressure by milking. Vaseline your hand and take off only sufficient milk to lessen the pressure. Don't empty the udders. Twelve hours later check again and if there is tightness repeat the milking. Once more take care not to over-milk. Feel the udders carefully. There should be no lumps. Should the teats have swollen or be painful or lumpy get your vet. Resist any recommendation to reduce milk production by hormone treatment. Supplies will get less by nature's own process. Worm the mare if you have not put her in foal again start work now by lungeing and quite soon you may ride her once again.

A SECOND FOAL

If your first foal has turned you on, that's great. The best time for a repeat is the foaling heat about nine days after birth. For easy reference, and for revision when you make this decision, I have summarised what you need to know and do in the Breeder's Calendar at the end of this book. If you have time just read this book through once more, add the improvements of your experience and go ahead.

I nearly forgot to remind you: keep your own diary right from the start. It will put everything into perspective — an interesting and useful record, a personal and permanent brief of your dreams, efforts, anxieties and joy.

THE BREEDER'S CALENDAR

DECEMBER
Scan through horse libraries and decide on your breeding manual.

JANUARY – MARCH
Select the stallion. See him and his progeny. Complete nomination form and fix date for arrival. Swab mare first heat in March.

APRIL – JULY
Take mare to stallion in April. Pregnancy test (June-July) at least forty-two days after successful service. Take mare home. Work out the foaling date: 340 days after last service.

JULY – SIX WEEKS BEFORE FOALING

SIX WEEKS TO GO
Prepare foaling box. Prepare and inspect paddock for danger to foal.

FIVE WEEKS TO GO
Reduce corn gradually to two-fifths at foaling time. Add a daily bran mash. Prepare the foaling bucket and equipment.

TWO WEEKS TO GO

Foaling imminent. Udder feels hard. A sticky off-white cork forms on the teats (waxing). Milk drips out. Softening and sinking of muscles around the hind quarters. "Falling in—poverty line". Swelling and softening of the vaginal lips. Enlargement of vaginal opening. Close to foaling: restlessness, scraping the straw, sweating, frequent droppings and urinating. But many give none of these signs.

FOALING SEQUENCE

Bursting of the water bag. Scrub up. The foal's feet appear. Decide whether position is normal: if not call vet. Feet and head appear. Clear nose of mucus. When dam strains to push out shoulders, assist by pulling foal's legs. As foal slips out, desist. Mare rests. Slide foal toward dam's head. Do not sever navel cord. Foal struggles. Cord breaks. Disinfect navel. Dry and massage the foal. Tie up placenta. Inspect for tears on vaginal opening; if severe call the vet. Bran mash for mare. Put clean straw on wet patches. Time for normal foaling: five to twenty-five minutes. If bleeding from navel persists, tie up. Foal must suck within six hours. If needed, assist. If unsuccessful (weak foal), milk mare and bottle feed after six hours. If foal still listless after second bottle, call vet. First droppings, four to five hours. Foal strains but no droppings; give enema. Placenta comes away within six hours; if not call the vet.

THE FIRST THREE WEEKS AFTER FOALING

After two or three days, first outing on fine day. Observance continues. Check navel; should be dry on third day. Mare's udder soft to touch. Foal should suck both nipples. If udder lumpy or hard, call vet. There is a normal discharge of blood from vaginal opening up to ten days. Foaling heat six to ten days after birth. Foal scours during heat. Should stop when dam has gone off. Watch foal's droppings. Diarrhoea is dangerous. Listen for conjested breathing and coughing. Foals have little resistance; call vet promptly. Introduce foal to oats at four months.

FIVE MONTHS AFTER FOALING

Wean the foal and feed oats. Ten hours after separation check dam's udders; if distended milk her. Never empty udders; only relieve pressure. Twelve hours later repeat. Check for lumps and swollen nipples. Worm mare and foal.

INDEX

36

NOTES

NOTES